John Cullen

y5y

John Cullen

Holly

OXFORD
UNIVERSITY PRESS

Great Clarendon Street, Oxford OX2 6DP

Oxford University Press is a department of the University of Oxford.
It furthers the University's objective of excellence in research, scholarship,
and education by publishing worldwide in

Oxford New York

Athens Auckland Bangkok Bogotá Buenos Aires Calcutta
Cape Town Chennai Dar es Salaam Delhi Florence Hong Kong Istanbul
Karachi Kuala Lumpur Madrid Melbourne Mexico City Mumbai
Nairobi Paris São Paulo Singapore Taipei Tokyo Toronto Warsaw

with associated companies in Berlin Ibadan

Oxford is a registered trade mark of Oxford University Press
in the UK and in certain other countries

British Library Cataloguing in Publication Data available

ISBN 0 19 276193 5 (hardback)
ISBN 0 19 276194 3 (paperback)

Typeset by Mary Tudge

Printed in Spain by Gráficas Estella, S.A.

WHIZZ BANG Orang-Utan

Rhymes for the very young

Compiled by **John Foster**

OXFORD

Contents

Whizz, Bang, Orang-Utan

Whizz, bang, orang-utan
Hear his mighty roar
As he stamps and he stomps
On the jungle floor.

There's a party in the jungle—
Everyone's there:
The elephant, the tiger,
And the little brown bear.

There's balloons and crackers,
Chocolates and cakes,
Ice-cream and jelly,
And raspberry milk-shakes.

Whizz, bang, orang-utan
Bends his knobbly knees,
Thumps his hairy chest,
As he dances through the trees.

John Foster

One Pink Sari

One pink sari for a pretty girl,
Two dancing women all in a whirl,
Three charmed cobras rising from a basket,
Four fat rubies, in the Rajah's casket,
Five water carriers straight and tall,
Six wicked vultures sitting on the wall,
Seven fierce tigers hiding in the grass,
Eight elephants rolling in a warm mud bath,
Nine green parrots in the coconut tree,
Ten twinkling stars, a-twinkling at me!

Ann Marie Linden

Miss Antrobus

Why do you love your octopus,
Miss Antrobus, Miss Antrobus?
Why do you love your octopus,
Miss Antrobus, my dear?

I love my octopus because
It hugs me and it wriggles.
I love my octopus because
Its wriggles give me giggles.
I love my octopus because
It juggles jars of pickles.
I love my octopus because
It tickles, oh, it tickles.

Richard Edwards

Serenade

Three mice sat down
in the barn one day
in a quiet corner
filled with hay.

One played a fiddle.
One played a drum.
One blew a bubble
with pink bubble gum.

Tra-la-la went the fiddle.
Boom, boom went the drum.
And POP! went the bubble
and the bubble gum.

Bobbi Katz

Little Pippa

Pip Pip Pippety Pip
Slid on the lino
Slippety Slip
Fell downstairs
Trippety Trip
Tore her knickers
Rippety Rip
Started to cry
Drippety Drip
Poor little Pippa
Pippety Pip.

Spike Milligan

Slippety slip

Trippety trip

Rippety rip

Drippety Drip

Adam Adam

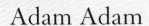

Adam Adam lost his shoe,
Mary Mary lost hers too,
Sara Sara found another,
Gave it to her baby brother,
Baby brother chewed the leather,
Baby sick, now all together;
Shoes shoes not for eating,
Shoes for putting smelly feet in.

Petonelle Archer

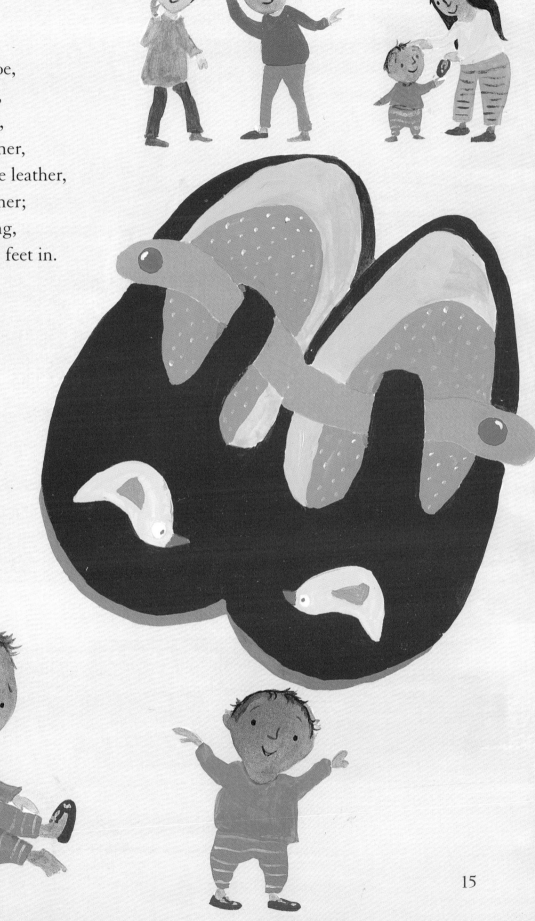

Miss Lucy Had a Baby

Miss Lucy had a baby.
She called him Tiny Tim.
She mixed some rum with mustard
And poured it over him,
But when the sun began to burn
And Tim began to cry
She wrapped him in newspaper
And hung him out to dry.

Traditional West Indian

Sons

A grumpy old woman named Rita
Had four naughty boys
All called Peter.
I once heard her say,
'Peter, please run away
And take Peter
And Peter
And Peter!'

Colleen Clancy

Slippery Sam

Slippery Sam
Bought a broom,
Ate an apple
And went to the moon;
Swept it clean,
Painted it red,
Came back to earth
And went to bed.

Arnold Spilka

Eileen Idle

Eileen Idle's eyebrows,
The hairiest of features,
Make the perfect hiding place
For shy little creatures.

Deep in Eileen's eyebrows
Fieldmice meet for talks,
And wrens enjoy a game of cards
Safe from sparrowhawks.

Richard Edwards

Mrs Matilda Mop

Mrs Matilda Mop
Fell asleep one day in a shop.
She awoke with a sneeze
And sat down on the peas
And the pods all started to **POP!**

to **POP**

to **POP**

TO POP!

to **POP**

to **POP**

to **POP**

Daphne Kitching

The Girl with the Marmalade Hair

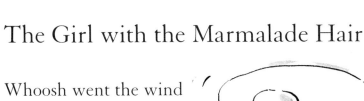

Whoosh went the wind
and up in the air
went a very small girl
with marmalade hair.

Boom went the wind
and a pig passing by
joined the small marmalade
girl in the sky.

They tumbled like leaves,
a peculiar pair.
'Hello,' said the girl
with the marmalade hair.

'Hello,' said the pig.
'Strange to travel like this,
but delightful to know
such a marmalade miss.'

'If we fly off to China
and back; we don't care,'
cried the pig and the girl
with the marmalade hair.

Marian Swinger

The Friendly Giant

The friendly giant
set off for town
and saw a car
had broken down.

He pushed it with
such giant power
it went two hundred
miles an hour.

He saw a farmer
making hay,
bent down and smiled
and said, 'Good day.'

His breath had such
a giant force
it blew the farmer
off his horse.

He hummed aloud
as he was strolling;
the sound was like
the thunder rolling.

The horses trembled
in the stable;
the dog shot under
the kitchen table.

He smiled and did
a little dance:
the earth shook all
the way to France,

and in the town
that lay beyond
the church spire crashed
into the pond.

He wandered up
the shopping street
(the lamp-posts snapped
beneath his feet).

He spoke (his grin
spread ear to ear):
'Hello, the friendly
giant is here.'

But nobody
came out to play—
for everyone
had run away!

Charles Thomson

21

Mrs McPhee

Mrs McPhee
Who lived in South Zeal
Roasted a duckling
For every meal.

'Duckling for breakfast
And dinner and tea,
And duckling for supper,'
Said Mrs McPhee.

'It's sweeter than sugar,
It's clean as a nut,
I'm sure and I'm certain
It's good for me—BUT

'I don't like these feathers
That grow on my back,
And my silly webbed feet
And my voice that goes quack.'

As easy and soft
As a ship to the sea,
As a duck to the water
Went Mrs McPhee.

'I think I'll go swim
In the river,' said she;
Said Mrs Mac, Mrs Quack,
Mrs McPhee.

Charles Causley

Arthur Ate an Apple

Arthur ate an apple.
He was about to eat another,
when an awful nasty thought
made him ask his aunty's mother,
'Are there in this apple
any angry little ants?'
'Oh no,' the woman answered,
'all the ants are in your pants!'

Michael Rosen

Three Cheers for Chips!

Chips are great!
Chips are ace!
Chips put a smile
on everyone's face.

Ice cream's yummy,
chocolate's nice,
but chips
are tops
at any
price!

Patricia Leighton

23

Victoria Nicola Liked to Eat

Victoria Nicola liked to eat:
Anything sweet was her favourite treat.
  The honey jar was sweet and sticky—
  Mmmm—sticky sticky Vicky Nicky.

Victoria Nicola liked to eat:
Anything sweet was her favourite treat.
  Asking for biscuits—cheery and cheeky
  Oh . . . sticky cheeky Vicky Nicky.

Victoria Nicola liked to eat:
Anything sweet was her favourite treat.
  The sugar spoon was lovely and licky—
  Mmmm . . . sticky cheeky licky Vicky Nicky.

Victoria Nicola liked to eat:
Anything sweet was her favourite treat.
Creeping in the kitchen, soft and sneaky
Aah . . . sticky cheeky licky sneaky Vicky Nicky.

Victoria Nicola liked to eat:
Anything sweet was her favourite treat.
Custard pan all yellow and thicky—
Mmmm . . . Oh-oh . . .
sticky
        cheeky
                licky
                        sneaky
                            sicky
                        Vicky Nicky.

Trevor Millum

Zing! Whizz! Ping!

Zing, whizz, ping,
Goes the popcorn in the pan.
Zing, whizz, ping,
Try and catch me, if you can.
Zing, whizz, ping,
Watch me hopping in the air.
Zing, whizz, ping,
You can eat me, if you dare.
But I'll make your tummy sing
With a zing, whizz, ping!

Cynthia Rider

Sugarcake Bubble

Sugarcake, sugarcake
  Bubbling in a pot
Bubble, bubble sugarcake
  Bubble thick and hot.

Sugarcake, sugarcake
  Spice and coconut
Sweet and sticky
  Brown and gooey.

I could eat the lot.

Grace Nichols

The Meal

Timothy Tompkins had turnips and tea.
The turnips were tiny.
He ate at least three.
And then, for dessert,
He had onions and ice.
He liked them so much
That he ordered it twice.
He had two cups of ketchup,
A prune, and a pickle.
'Delicious,' said Timothy.
'Well worth a nickel.'
He folded his napkin
And hastened to add,
'It's one of the loveliest breakfasts I've had.'

Karla Kuskin

Something in my Soup

'What's that in my soup, Mummy?'
'Oh no, it's the baby's dummy!'

Charles Thomson

Cabbage

Sometimes Grandma gives me things
I do not like to eat,
Cabbage leaves with soggy strings
And slimy luncheon meat.
I push them round and round the plate
And when she isn't looking
I stuff into my wellingtons
The worst of Grandma's cooking.

Jean Willis

There Was an Old Lady

There was an old lady
 Whose kitchen was bare,
So she called for the cat
 Saying, 'Time for some air!'

She sent him to buy her
 A packet of cheese.
But the cat hurried back
 With a basket of bees.

She sent him to buy her
 A gallon of juice.
But the cat reappeared
 With a galloping goose.

She sent him to buy her
 A dinner of beef.
But the cat scampered home
 With an Indian chief.

She sent him to buy her
  A bowl of ice cream.
But the cat skated in
  With a whole hockey team.

She sent him to buy her
  A bite of spaghetti.
But the cat strutted up
  With a bride and confetti.

She sent him to buy her
  A fine cup of tea.
But the cat waddled back
  With a dinosaur's knee.

The fridge was soon bulging,
  And so was the shelf.
So she sent for a hot dog
  And ate it herself.

Dennis Lee

Helter-Skelter

On my mat of coconut
whizzing round and round
trailing streams of corkscrew screams
till I reach the ground.

Gina Douthwaite

At the Funfair

I rode on the roller coaster,
    I thought it would never stop.
It was scary and very exciting
    especially right at the top.

The houses and shops looked like Lego,
    below me were small coloured cars.
The thrills and the spills of the funfair
    made me dizzy as wandering stars!

John Rice

Down at the Dinosaur Fair

You can turn,
you can twist
in the prehistoric mist,
feel the dampness in your hair.
You can sprint,
you can spin
from a big bony chin
   down at the Dinosaur Fair!

You can swoop,
you can swing
from a dark leather wing
and fly through pillows of air.
You can slip,
you can slide
on a scaly scarlet hide
   down at the Dinosaur Fair!

DINOSAUR FAIR

You can zing,
you can zoom
down a backbone flume,
whizz round in a waltzing chair.
You can whip,
you can whack
on a slippy saddle back
  down at the Dinosaur Fair!

You can trip,
you can trek
up a narrow bendy neck
any day, any time, any where.
You can flail,
you can float
like a wave-tossed boat
  down at the Dinosaur Fair!

John Rice

On Hallowe'en

We mask our faces
and wear strange hats
and moan like witches
and screech like cats
and jump like goblins
and thump like elves
and almost manage
to scare *ourselves*.

Aileen Fisher

36

O Witches and Wizards

O witches and wizards, where have you been?
　We've been to a party for old Hallowe'en.

A Hallowe'en party! O what did you eat?
　Spiced turnip lanterns and hot cauldron treat.

And after the eating what games did you play?
　Old Spells, Hokey-Pokey, and Scare-Them-Away.

And after the game did you all dance together?
　We danced like the North wind in rough, stormy weather.

O witches and wizards, what else did you do?
　Ah, that is our secret. We cannot tell you.

Cynthia Mitchell

The Castle

There's a castle under the table in the lounge
With bats and owls;
Its walls may look like cardboard
And its doors like bathroom towels,
But that is just a trick to fool the dragons' beady eyes
For the castle under the table in the lounge
Is in disguise.

There's a castle under the table in the lounge
With one dark cell
Where every day my wizard, Wex,
Invents a different spell.
Today it's one to turn invaders slowly into stone;
There's a castle under the table in the lounge:
Leave it alone!

There's a castle under the table in the lounge
With steps that go
Through miles of smoky nothingness
To secret caves below
Where blacksmiths forge intruder-traps that snap with teeth of tin;
There's a castle under the table in the lounge:
You can't come in!

There's a castle under the table in the lounge
With seven towers
Where seven fair princesses sing
To seven lutes for hours,
And seven servants guard their doors with seven snarling hounds;
There's a castle under the table in the lounge;
It's out of bounds!

There's a castle under the table in the lounge
In which I hide
While dragons calling, 'Tea-time! Tea-time!'
Lumber by outside—
As if I'd fall for that one, no, I'm staying here all day,
In my castle under the table in the lounge,
So keep away!

Richard Edwards

Paint on my Nose

There's paint on my nose,
And away it won't scrape.
I've tried using soap,
And detergent and tape.
I've tried using lemons,
I've even tried pears,
But I look in the mirror
And see it still there.

I've rubbed it with wax,
Wool, and plastic and leather,
But I fear it won't move,
And I'm painted forever.
And wherever I go,
People say, 'There he goes.
It's that boy who just can't
Get the paint off his nose.'

Clive Riche

40

Em's Empty Egg

When Em's given egg she gets cracking
There's egg all over her face
Egg in her hair, egg in her ears
Egg all over the place
My dad says it's just cos she's little
And hasn't yet learned to be neat
But I think it's how she makes certain
There's no egg in her egg to eat

Hiawyn Oram

Yuck!

Jam all over her fingers,
pastry in her hair,
fruit juice dribbling down her chin
and custard everywhere.

Playdough in her fingernails,
mud between her toes,
and something much, much nastier
running from her nose.

But none of that would bother me,
if it weren't for this:
my sister's heading this way fast
and it's *me* she wants to kiss.

Paul Rogers

42

My Baby Sister

My baby sister's
really swell.
I love her smile
but not her smell.

Bruce Lansky

43

This Tooth

I jiggled it
   jaggled it
   jerked it.

I pushed
   and pulled
   and poked it.

 But—

As soon as I stopped,
and left it alone,
this tooth came out
on its very own!

Lee Bennett Hopkins

44

As Long As I Please

I want to
Grow my hair
As long as I please.
I want to
Grow my hair
Down to my knees.
I don't care
For fashion and hats.
I just want to
Sit on my plaits.

Alan Bagnall

Today's My Birthday

Today's my birthday.
Now I'm four.
I'm one year older
Than I was before.

I measured myself
Against the wall
And I'm over a hundred
Centimetres tall—

Much taller than
I used to be,
When I was small
And only three.

Today's my birthday.
Now I'm four.
I'm older and bigger
Than I was before.

John Foster

Birthdays

If birthdays happened once a week
Instead of once a year,
Think of all the gifts you'd get
And all the songs you'd hear,
And think how quickly you'd grow up;
Wouldn't it feel queer
If birthdays happened once a week
Instead of once a year?

Mary Ann Hoberman

On Being Five

I am five and it's my birthday
Bounce, bounce, bounce.
I won't wear my party dress
Flounce, flounce, flounce.

Cakes and crisps are on the table
Jelly and ice-cream.
Sara wants to eat it now
Scream, scream, scream.

It's my birthday, it's my birthday,
Streamers in the hall.
It's my party, it's my party,
Mummy up the wall.

I am five and I've got presents
I want more.
George has spread the chocolate icing
On the floor.

Daddy thinks the clown is funny
So does Aunty Sue,
Amy thinks the clown is scary
Boo hoo hoo!

Bradley won the pass the parcel
It's not fair,
It's *my* birthday, *I* get presents,
Pull his hair.

It's my birthday, what a party!
When I'm six years old
I've promised everyone I will be
Good as gold.

Petonelle Archer

49

Bouncing Ben

Bouncing Ben bounced on the bed,
Bounced to the ceiling and banged his head.

Bouncing Ben landed on the floor.
Bouncing Ben with his bottom sore.

Bouncing Ben lying on his bed,
A bump on his bottom and a lump on his head.

John Foster

I Won't

I won't, no I won't, no I won't do that.
I don't want to. I don't have to.
No I won't wear that hat.

I hate it, yes I hate it, yes I hate hate hate.
You can't make me. I don't want to.
I don't care if we are late.

Yes I'm naughty, yes I'm naughty.
Yes I know, know, know.
But I won't wear that hat
So it's No! No! No!

Michelle Magorian

Accidental ABC

A is for Accidents
(Spilling my food)
It's *splat* on the floor
And now Mum's in a mood.

B is for Bruises
(on *both* of my knees)
Mum says it's my fault
For climbing up trees.

But C is for Cuddles
(Mum holding me tight)
When monsters and bears
Come for me in the night.

Lucy Coats

Wizard Bear

If you trap your fingers in the door,
Or fall and bang your knee on the floor,
Who's always there to cuddle and care?
Wizard Bear.

If you hear a noise during the night,
Have a bad dream and wake with a fright,
Who's always there to cuddle and care?
Wizard Bear.

If you're full of cold, lying in bed,
With a runny nose and aching head,
Who's always there to cuddle and care?
Wizard Bear.

If you're down in the dumps, feeling sad,
If you've done something naughty and bad,
Who's always there to cuddle and care?
Wizard Bear.

John Foster

53

Mama, Papa, and Baby Joe

Under over Coca-Cola
Off to Pick 'n' Pay we go,
Moany moany macaroni,
Mama, Papa, and Baby Joe.

Harum-scarum through the traffic
Ziggery-zaggery park the car.
Bumpity-bump along the pavement
Around the block and there you are!

In and out the shops so busy
Mama and Papa go yackety-yack.
See you later, escalator
Okey-dokey, clickety-clack . . .

54

Spaghetti falling pitter-pat,
Hot and bothered screaming Mama
'DON'T DO THAT!' **'DON'T DO THAT!'**

Checkout lady checks the shopping
Money honey jingle jam,
Papa, Mama in a tizzy
Boogie-woogie in the pram! . . .

In Fatty Boom Boom's Take Away,
Sticky icky licking baby
Mama smiling, it's OK! . . .

Shopping packed and home we go!
Honky-tonky through the city
Mama, Papa, and sleepy Joe.

Niki Daly

A Day at School

In the morning, there's a muddle,
just the same as every day
then we're registered and sorted
and she sends us off to play
I can put the bricks together
I can pull them all apart
I can make a house, a tiger,
or a picture-horse and cart
I can build a giant's tower
with its top up in the sky
I can make an aeroplane that
flaps its wings to make it fly
and outside the wind is blowing
and it blows me from behind
and it makes me run and run and
shuts my eyes and makes me blind
I'm a hunter in the jungle
and I'm hunting for a bear
and I'll fight it with a ruler
when I find it in its lair
now I'm creeping through a forest
tippy-toeing like a mouse
and I'll steal the children's toys back
from the wicked witch's house

56

now it's in-time and the bell rings
story-time now on the mat
with the alphabet in colour
and the cat who wears a hat
now we're back inside the classroom
and the big ones do their sums
but we're little so we're playing
and we're playing Dads and Mums
I don't want to be a Daddy
I'm a creepy slimy thing
with a hundred legs and whiskers
and a great big purple STING!

Jessie Thomas

Cats

One cat, two cats, three cats, four,
Four cats scratching
At my gran's back door.

Five cats, six cats, seven cats, eight,
Eight cats scratching
At my grandma's gate.

Eight cats, seven cats, six cats, five,
Five cats scratching
At the old bee-hive.

Four cats, three cats, two cats, one,
One cat napping
In the noon-day sun.

John Kitching

There was a young girl called Maggie

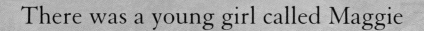

There was a young girl called Maggie
Whose dog was enormous and shaggy.
   The front end of him
   Looked vicious and grim—
But the tail end was friendly and waggy.

Anon.

Puppy

Here is our puppy, a black and white romper,
A bustler, a bouncer, a champion jumper;
A racer, a chaser, who never stops saying,
It's great being a puppy, it's all barking and playing.

Jack Ousbey

Summer

I lie on my back
And look at the sky,
As clouds like elephants
Roll on by.
The sun is warm,
A cool wind blows,
I can smell the scent
Of the sweet red rose.
The bumble bees hum,
A bird shrilly sings,
The crickets chirrup
As summer brings
Strawberries and raspberries
And blackberries too,
Poppies and buttercups
And cornflower blue.

Ann Marie Linden

Berry Picking

Strawberries,
  strawberries—
yum, yum, yummy!
One for the pail
and
one for the tummy!

One to save
and
one to taste—
lots to pick
and
none to waste!

Bobbi Katz

Watching a Bumble Bee

Out in the garden
   you will see
the oh-so-busy
   bumble bee.

It never stops to
   take a rest.
It wears an oh-so-hairy
   vest.

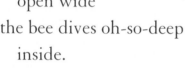

When flowers, in summer,
   open wide
the bee dives oh-so-deep
   inside.

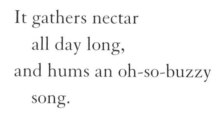

It gathers nectar
   all day long,
and hums an oh-so-buzzy
   song.

While you watch from your
   garden seat
the bee makes honey
   oh-so-sweet.

Then off it zigzags
   in a tizz
with an oh-so-busy
   buzzy
      whizzzzzzzzzzzzzzz

Wes Magee

zzzzzzzzzzzZZZZZZZZZzzzzzzZZZZZZzz

Caterpillar

Creepy crawly caterpillar
Looping up and down,
Furry tufts of hair upon
Your back of golden brown.

You will soon be wrapped in silk,
Asleep for many a day;
And then, a handsome butterfly,
You'll stretch and fly away.

Mary Dawson

63

A Tree House

A tree house,
A me house,
A hide away and see house.

A lizard house,
A bird house,
A leave the world beneath house.

A yelling house,
A singing house,
A quiet as a mouse house.

A green house,
A dream house,
An only you and me house.

A whatever you want to be house—
A tree house.

Donna D. Cooner

The Shadow Tree

I'd love to sit
On the highest branch
But it's much too high
For me;

So I sit in the grass
Where the shadow falls,
On top of
The shadow tree.

Ilo Orleans

The Chestnut Tree

The chestnut tree's like a giant umbrella,
And when it rains I can shelter there,
All around the raindrops are falling,
But I'm all dry in my great green lair!

Daphne Lister

The Garden Path

The garden path at Grandma's
Leads past the little pond,
Where nimble golden fishes hide,
To tunnelled leaves beyond.

And through the jungly bit you find
A gate beside a tree,
And a huge world made of grass and sky
As far as you can see.

Shirley Hughes

Pony

Clip-clop, swing along,
Swish-a-tail, neigh,
Pony in the meadow
Is up and away;
Frolicking and frisking,
As if to say,
It's a kick-a-leg, shake-a-mane,
Swish-a-tail day.

Jack Ousbey

67

The Cow Who Liked Jumping

There once was a cow
With great good sense,
Jumped over a gate
And over a fence,

Over a river,
Over a tree,
Over a mountain,
Over a sea,

Over a jungle,
Over a plain,
Over a forest
And back again,

Back to her field
And the same old ways,
Chewing the grass
In a bit of a daze.

So was she content
With the usual scene?
Did she go back
To her normal routine?

NO!

She went for the Big One,
Yes, one afternoon
Daisy the Cow
Jumped over the moon!

June Crebbin

Feeding Ducks with Grandad

When Grandad takes us to the park
We always take some bread,
He says before we have some fun
The ducks must all be fed.

And when the ducks have all been fed,
Too full to flap their wings,
Then Grandad races really fast
To beat us to the swings.

Coral Rumble

70

At the Park

At the park
I like to have:

a diving fling
on a flying swing,

a quick funnel
through a dark tunnel,

a slippery glide
down a shooting slide,

and a whirling flier
on a twirling tyre.

But best of all:

is being dizzily wound about
on a busily spinning roundabout!

Ian Souter

A Corner of Magic

There's a park near our house
With the usual park things:
Lots of dogs, mums with babies,
A roundabout and swings.

It's scruffy, and it's dirty,
And I don't like it much;
The roundabout's squeaky
And cold to the touch.

But down in the corner,
By a tumbledown wall,
There's some trees and some bushes
Where I once lost a ball.

It was quiet and gloomy,
It was dark, it was cold
And it felt like a place
That was creepy and old.

It felt like a forest
Full of powerful things . . .
Where a prince might have searched
For a magical ring,

I shuddered, I shivered,
I felt very cold,
As I thought of the stories
Those trees could have told.

I turned and ran out,
To people and light,
And my dad said I looked like
I'd had a real fright.

Where a witch fought a wizard,
Where a battle took place,
Where a princess and a pauper
Once hid in disgrace . . .

In the heart of the city,
In that scruffy old park,
There's a corner of magic,
Of mystery and dark.

We sometimes go back there,
And I play on the swings;
But I'll leave my lost ball
To those magical things . . .

Tony Bradman

73

In August

When the sun is strong
    And the day is hot,
We move around
    At a peaceful trot.

We don't wear much
    In the way of clothes
And we squirt ourselves
    With a garden hose.

Marchette Chute

74

Seaside

Sand in the sandwiches,
　　Sand in the tea,
Flat, wet sand running
　　Down to the sea.
Pools full of seaweed,
　　Shells and stones,
Damp bathing-suits
　　And ice-cream cones.

Waves pouring in
　　To a sand-castle moat.
Mend the defences!
　　Now we're afloat!
Water's for splashing,
　　Sand is for play,
A day by the sea
　　Is the best kind of day.

Shirley Hughes

Change in the Weather

I think it would be very good
To have some snow and sleet
In summer when
We need it most
To drive away the heat.

Ilo Orleans

If I Could Be a Pilot

If I could be a pilot
Each Christmas Eve I'd fly
To fetch a fluffy snow cloud
From the distant Arctic sky,
I'd chase it, catch it, tow it home
And tie it to a tree,
So snow would fall on Christmas Day
On all my friends and me.

Richard Edwards

76

Christmas Eve

When Mummy tucked me into bed
She hung the stocking near my head,
And 'Close your eyes and sleep,' she said,
 And shut the door.

Although it's dark my eyes are bright
And I can see without the light;
I'm going to stay awake all night
 To watch who comes.

Listen, I hear the floorboards crack!
It must be Santa with his sack!
A face looms near and then draws back.
 It's only Dad.

Next time I raise my head to peep,
Presents are lying in a heap!
And I haven't even been to sleep!
 How does he do it?

Brian Levison

A Winter Parcel

Today I'm like a parcel,
wrapped up from top to toe,
protected from the icy winds,
the rain, the sleet, the snow.

My head has got a hat on,
my neck hides in a scarf,
and on my hands are puppet gloves,
a tiger and giraffe.

My coat is thick and furry,
and does up very high,
and on my feet I've special boots,
to keep me warm and dry.

So though there's little of me
that anyone can see,
this walking, talking parcel is
most definitely ME!

Linda Hammond

Knitting

Our budgie's wearing bootees,
our puppy's wearing mittens,
there's a warm scarf on our cat,
and cardies on our kittens,
our goldfish wears a beanie
though I fear it doesn't fit,
and all because my grandma
loves to sit and knit and knit.

Nigel Gray

79

Winter Morning

It's sleeting, it's snowing,
a north wind is blowing,
my ears are red,
my fingers feel dead,
and my cherry-red nose is glowing.

Nigel Gray

Doctor Foster

Doctor Foster went to Gloucester
On a winter's day.
An icicle froze
On the end of his nose
And didn't fall off till May.

Richard Edwards

Galoshes

Susie's galoshes
Make splishes and sploshes
And slooshes and sloshes
As Susie steps slowly
Along in the slush.

They stamp and they tramp
On the ice and concrete,
They get stuck in the muck and the mud;
But Susie likes much best to hear

The slippery slush
As it slooshes and sloshes
And splishes and sploshes
All round her galoshes!

Rhoda Bacmeister

81

Bedtime, Teddytime

It's bedtime, it's teddytime,
it's pyjamas at the readytime.

It's bedtime, it's tunetime,
it's watch the milky moontime.

It's bedtime, it's blisstime,
it's one more goodnight kisstime.

John Rice

Cubby

Grandma has a lion cub
With worn-out ears and fur,
It once belonged to a little boy
Who used to live with her.
That little boy was my father,
It gives me such a thrill
To think that his kisses and cuddles
Are stuck to the lion cub still.

Jean Willis

82

Wee Willie Winkie

Wee Willie Winkie runs through the town,
upstairs and downstairs in his nightgown,
the wind's very chilly—he's shivering like a jelly:
are the children in their beds?

No, they're watching telly!

Nigel Gray

O My Grand Old Granpa York

O My Grand Old Granpa York
He had ten thousand teds,
He marched them into their baths every night,
Then he marched them to their beds.
And when they got in they were wet,
And when they got out they were dry,
And when they were all snuggled up very tight
He sang them a lullaby.

Lucy Coats

Sailing to Sea

I'm sailing to sea in the bathroom,
  And I'm swimming to sea in a tub,
And the only song that I ever will sing
  Is rub-a-dub dub-a-dub dub.

A duck and a dog and a submarine
  Are sailing together with me,
And it's rub-a-dub-dub
And it's dub-a-dub-dub
  As we sail out to sea.

Dennis Lee

The Dark

I don't like the dark coming down on my head
It feels like a blanket thrown over the bed
I don't like the dark coming down on my head

I don't like the dark coming down over me
It feels like the room's full of things I can't see
I don't like the dark coming down over me

There isn't enough light from under the door
It only just reaches the edge of the floor
There isn't enough light from under the door

I wish that my dad hadn't put out the light
It feels like there's something that's just out of sight
I wish that my dad hadn't put out the light

But under the bedclothes it's warm and secure
You can't see the ceiling, you can't see the floor
Yes, under the bedclothes it's warm and secure
So I think I'll stay here till it's daylight once more.

Adrian Henri

Bedtime Song

The stars above are glittering
   The moon is gleaming bright
And noisy cats are singing songs
   Down in the yard tonight
     MIAOW WOW WOW
        WOW WOW

People in their dressing-gowns
   In houses far and near
Are leaning from their window sills
   They're horrified to hear
     MIAOW WOW WOW
        WOW WOW

But we don't want a lullaby
   We prefer a din
Noisy cats are what we like—
   All join in!
     MIAOW WOW WOW
        WOW WOW
          WOW WOW

Quentin Blake

Nighty Night

Nighty night
Sleepy tight,
Don't let those buggies bite.
If they bite
(And some of them do)
Smack their behinds
With the sole of your shoe.

Lucy Coats

Index of titles and first lines

First lines are shown in *italics*

Acknowledgements

We would like to thank the following for permission to include their poems, published here for the first time:
Petonelle Archer: 'Adam Adam' and 'On Being Five', © Petonelle Archer 1999. **Lucy Coats**: 'Accidental ABC', © Lucy Coats 1999.
Gina Douthwaite: 'Helter-Skelter', © Gina Douthwaite 1999. **John Foster**: 'Whizz Bang, Orang-Utan', 'Today's My Birthday',
'Bouncing Ben', 'Wizard Bear', 'It's Snowed', and 'Lullaby', all © John Foster 1999. **Nigel Gray**: 'Winter Morning', 'Knitting',
'Wee Willie Winkie', all © Nigel Gray 1999. **Bobbi Katz**: 'Serenade', © Bobbi Katz 1999. **Daphne Kitching**: 'Mrs Matilda Mop',
© Daphne Kitching 1999. **John Kitching**: 'Cats', © John Kitching 1999. **Patricia Leighton**: 'Three Cheers for Chips' and
'The Candyfloss Man', both © Patricia Leighton 1999. **Daphne Lister**: 'The Chestnut Tree', © Daphne Lister 1999. **Wes Magee**:
'Watching a Bumble Bee', © Wes Magee 1999. **Trevor Millum**: 'Victoria Nicola Liked to Eat', © Trevor Millum 1999. **Jack Ousbey**:
'Puppy' and 'Pony', both © Jack Ousbey 1999. **John Rice**: 'At the Funfair', 'Down at the Dinosaur Fair', and 'Bedtime, Teddytime',
all © John Rice 1999. **Clive Riche**: 'Paint on my Nose', © Clive Riche 1999. **Cynthia Rider**: 'Zing! Whizz! Ping!', © Cynthia Rider
1999. **Coral Rumble**: 'Feeding Ducks with Grandad', © Coral Rumble 1999. **Ian Souter**: 'At the Park', © Ian Souter 1999. **Marian
Swinger**: 'The Girl with the Marmalade Hair', © Marian Swinger 1999. **Jessie Thomas**: 'A Day at School', © Jessie Thomas 1999.
Charles Thomson: 'The Friendly Giant' and 'Something in my Soup', both © Charles Thomson 1999.

We are also grateful for permission to include the following poems:
Quentin Blake: 'Bedtime Song' from *All Join In* (Red Fox), by permission of A. P. Watt Ltd on behalf of Quentin Blake. **Tony
Bradman**: 'A Corner of Magic' from *Smile Please* (Penguin, 1987) by permission of the author. **Charles Causley**: 'Mrs McPhee' from
Early in the Morning (Viking Kestrel), by permission of David Higham Associates. **Marchette Chute**: 'In August' from *Around and
About* by Marchette Chute, © 1957 by E P Dutton, © renewed 1985 by Marchette Chute, by permission of Elizabeth Hauser.
Colleen Clancy: 'Sons' from *Big Dipper*, edited by June Epstein, June Factor, Gwendda McKay, and Dorothy Rickards (OUP,
Australia) by permission of the editors as copyright holders. **Lucy Coats**: 'Nighty Night' and 'O My Grand Old Granpa York'
from *First Rhymes* (first published in the UK in 1994 by Orchard Books, a division of the Watts Publishing Group), by permission
of the publishers. **Donna Cooner**: 'A Tree House' from *Spider* July 1996, Volume 3, No. 7. **June Crebbin**: 'The Cow Who Liked
Jumping' from *Cows Moo, Cars Toot!* (Viking, 1995), © June Crebbin 1995, by permission of Penguin Books Ltd. **Niki Daly**: lines
from *Mama, Papa and Baby Joe* (Bodley Head), © Niki Daly 1992, by permission of Random House UK Ltd and the author, c/o
Laura Cecil Literary Agency. **Mary Dawson**: 'Caterpillar' from *Sit on the Roof and Holler* (Bell & Hyman, 1984), © Mary Dawson
1984, by permission of the author. **Richard Edwards**: 'If I could be a Pilot' from *If Only . . .* (Puffin, 1991), 'Miss Antrobus' and
'Eileen Idle' from *Teaching the Parrot* (Faber, 1996), 'Doctor Foster' from *Nonsense Nursery Rhymes* (OUP, 1997), and 'The Castle'
from Richard Edwards (ed.): *Ten Golden Years* (Walker); all poems © Richard Edwards, and by permission of the author. **Aileen
Fisher**: 'On Hallowe'en' from *Out in the Dark and Daylight* (HarperCollins), © Aileen Fisher 1980, by permission of Marian Reiner
for the author. **Linda Hammond**: 'A Winter Parcel' from *One Blue Boat* (Viking, 1991), © Linda Hammond 1991, by permission of
Penguin Books Ltd. **Adrian Henri**: 'The Dark' from *The Rhinestone Rhino* (Methuen, 1989), © Adrian Henri 1989, by permission
of the author c/o Rogers, Coleridge & White Ltd, 20 Powis Mews, London W11 1JN. **Mary Ann Hoberman**: 'Birthdays' from Jack
Prelutsky (ed.): *Walker Book of Poetry for Children*. **Shirley Hughes**: 'The Garden Path' from *Rhymes for Annie
Rose* (Red Fox), by permission of Random House UK Ltd; 'Seaside' from *Out and About*, © Shirley Hughes
1988, by permission of the publisher, Walker Books Ltd, London. **Bobbi Katz**: 'Berry Picking' from
Poems for Small Friends (Random House, 1989), © Random House, by permission of the author.
Karla Kuskin: 'The Meal' from *Alexander Soames: His Poems*, © 1962, 1980 by Karla Kuskin,
by permission of Scott Treimel New York. **Bruce Lansky**: 'My Baby Sister' from *Poetry
Party* (Meadowbrook Press, 1996), © Bruce Lansky 1996, by permission of the author
and publishers. **Dennis Lee**: 'There Was an Old Lady' and 'Sailing to Sea' from *Jelly
Belly* (Macmillan of Canada, 1983), © Dennis Lee 1983, by permission of the author c/o
Westwood Creative Artists. **Brian Levison**: 'Christmas Eve' first published in Moira Andrew
(ed.): *Where Wild Things Grow* (Macmillan Education, 1988), by permission of the author. **Anne Marie
Linden**: 'One Pink Sari' and 'Summer' both from *Steel Drums* (BBC Books), by permission of the author.
Colin MacNaughton: 'If I Had a Monster' from *Making Friends with Frankenstein*, © Colin MacNaughton

1993, by permission of the publisher, Walker Books Ltd, London. **Michelle Magorian**: 'I Won't' from *Waiting for My Shorts to Dry* (Viking Kestrel, 1989) © Michelle Magorian 1989, by permission of Penguin Books Ltd and the author c/o Rogers, Coleridge & White Ltd, 20 Powis Mews, London W11 1JN. **Spike Milligan**: 'Little Pippa' from *Little Pot Boiler* (Puffin), by permission of Spike Milligan Productions Ltd. **Grace Nichols**: 'Sugarcake Bubble' from *No Hickory, No Dickory, No Dock* (Puffin), © Grace Nichols 1991, by permission of Curtis Brown Ltd, London, on behalf of the author. **Hiawyn Oram**: 'Em's Empty Egg' from *Speaking for Ourselves* (Methuen, 1990), © Hiawyn Oram 1990, by permission of the author c/o Rogers, Coleridge & White Ltd, 20 Powis Mews, London W11 1JN. **Ilo Orleans**: 'Change in the Weather' from *Surprise* compiled by Lee Bennett Hopkins (Heinemann), and 'The Shadow Tree' from *Knickerbocker Number Nine* edited by Richard Brown and Kate Ruttle (Cambridge University Press), both by permission of Karen S. Solomon. **Paul Rogers**: 'Yuck!' from *Yuck!* (Nelson, 1993), © Paul Rogers 1993, by permission of the author. **Michael Rosen**: 'Arthur Ate an Apple' from *Michael Rosen's ABC* (Macdonald Young Books, 1987), © Michael Rosen 1987, by permission of The Peters Fraser & Dunlop Group Ltd on behalf of Michael Rosen. **Jean Willis**: 'Cabbage' and 'Cubby' both from *Toffee Pockets* (Bodley Head), by permission of Random House UK Ltd.

Despite every effort to trace and contact copyright holders before publication this has not been possible in all cases. If notified the publisher will be pleased to rectify any errors or omissions at the earliest opportunity.

Cover illustration: **Tony Ross**

Inside illustrations:
Jon Berkeley pp. 22–23, 32–33, 52–53, 66–67
Debbie Boon pp. 26–27, 40–41, 74–75
Ian Cunliffe pp. 28–29, 36–37, 68–69
James Faulkner pp. 30–31, 78–79, 82–83
Serena Feneziani pp. 18–19, 46–47, 72–73, 84–85
Lindsey Gardiner pp. 16–17, 24–25, 44–45, 50–51
Sue Heap pp. 14–15, 34–35, 42–43
Stephen Lambert pp. 60–61, 86–87
Joanne Partis pp. 58–59, 62–63, 88–89
Susan Rollings pp. 56–57, 70–71, 80–81
Tony Ross pp. 2–9, 90–95
Nick Schon pp. 12–13, 20–21, 48–49, 54–55
Stephen Waterhouse pp. 10–11, 38–39, 64–65, 76–77

Lullaby

The stars have switched their lights on.
Day's curtains have been drawn.
The birds are resting in the trees.
There's dew upon the lawn.

The toys are in their boxes.
The stories have been read.
It's time for drifting off to sleep
Tucked safely up in bed.

John Foster